GERIATRIC
CONTENTMENT
A Guide to Its Achievement in
Your Home

Geriatric
Contentment

A Guide To Its Achievement In
Your Home

By

SHIRLEY G. DESNICK, B.A., O.T.R.

CHARLES C THOMAS • PUBLISHER
Springfield • Illinois • U.S.A.

Published and Distributed Throughout the World by
CHARLES C THOMAS • PUBLISHER
BANNERSTONE HOUSE
301-327 East Lawrence Avenue, Springfield, Illinois, U.S.A.
NATCHEZ PLANTATION HOUSE
735 North Atlantic Boulevard, Fort Lauderdale, Florida, U.S.A.

With THOMAS BOOKS *careful attention is given to all details of
manufacturing and design. It is the Publisher's desire to present books
that are satisfactory as to their physical qualities and artistic possibilities
and appropriate for their particular use.* THOMAS BOOKS *will be true
to those laws of quality that assure a good name and good will.*

Printed in the United States of America
A-2

PREFACE

GERIATRIC CONTENTMENT is written for those who are privileged to be entrusted with the care of the elderly, both healthy and otherwise. It will also provide insight and guidance to those who frequently find themselves in the company of the elderly, either socially or as advisors. Lastly, for one who *intends* to be numbered among the elderly himself, one day, it provides some guidelines for development of attitudes and future behavior.

So much has been said about the lack of adequate care afforded the elderly. In *Geriatric Contentment* we have the evidence that this is not the case in many homes, and that it need not be the case in most others.

Since most people who care for the elderly may have had very little professional training for their jobs, *Geriatric Contentment* contains few, if any, technical words. It is written in simple, practical terms, but designed so that people of all levels of responsibility can study it together. Thus they can learn to appreciate each other's jobs and build toward the maximum cooperation required for an ideal resident-staff relationship.

Frequently observed reactions of hundreds of older adults have been taken into account as methods of handling them are discussed. Section One is devoted to suggestions for smooth day-to-day operation of a nursing home or home for the aged. All ideas presented in this book are based upon the unconditional assumption that we hold the elderly in the highest esteem. We respect them for their individual accomplishments and for what their entire generation has left us as a legacy. We also respect their right to live each of their remaining years to the fullest of their capacities, even as we expect this for ourselves.

Section Two is devoted to suggestions for unusual, stimulating recreational projects. Precisely because they are not the type of activities most of us think of in connection with the elderly, it is hoped that many staffs will venture to use them. Each one has been tried and tested, and proved to be unusually successful. Descriptions include not merely the mechanical execution of the projects but how, if interpreted properly, each one can have a beneficial effect on the overall atmosphere and operation of the home.

Reading this book helps one to see the essential part each employee plays in the development of a contented resident. It helps him to see that no employee works in a vacuum. His actions and words become entwined with those of others. Since happiness and contentment are contagious, we urge you to follow the guidelines in *Geriatric Contentment* to attain happy and contented staff members *and* residents.

INTRODUCTION

THERE COMES A TIME in the lives of some people when it is no longer feasible for them to live alone or with their children. Many of these people enter homes for the aged or nursing homes.

Becoming a resident in such a home holds the promise of peace and contentment for many years to come. It means freedom from concerns about household chores, personal care, and loneliness. Even more than that, it can provide an extension of the joy and fulfillment of earlier years when new friendships, new experiences, and new accomplishments made each day something to look forward to.

To accomplish these goals we operate on the basic premise that everyone responds to warmth and sincerity. And homes with wise staffs take advantage of the fact that happiness is contagious. There are probably few jobs which require more versatility than working with the aged, since our warmth and sincerity must assume so many different forms. We must often behave quite differently with each resident, depending upon whether he is physically ill, mentally ill, or not ill at all. But what is equally important, we must be ready to change our behavior as he moves from one condition to another, and strive to help him to make these transitions.

The overall atmosphere in the happiest homes is based upon the assumption that everyone is well and capable of living life to the fullest. As we acquire specific information from medical records or personal contacts which indicate modifications required in individual cases, we act accordingly.

Whatever his level of attainment may be at any stage, we help him to appreciate it and make the most of it.

ACKNOWLEDGMENTS

M UCH OF THE CREDIT for the choice of the activities described in this book goes to Gunnar H. Cronstrom, Administrator of Park Nursing Home in St. Louis Park, Minnesota. It was his cooperative and enterprising spirit, plus his sincere desire to add to the contentment of his residents, which made it possible for me to develop these projects.

To Mrs. Margaret Ulinder, beauty operator at the Park Nursing Home, I am grateful for an uncanny insight into the needs and wishes of the elderly, which she so freely shared with me. To the many nurses, aides, and orderlies at "Park" who allowed me, knowingly or not, to observe the effects of various methods of handling the residents, I say "Thank you."

And many thanks to the members of my own household, each for a different reason. To my eighty-three year old mother, for allowing me to experience very intimately the effects of the years on the ability of the body to function, and its accompanying effects on one's outlook on life. To my daughters Beth, Julie, Laurel and Rochelle for their reactions to my ideas, plus refreshing suggestions untainted by preconceived misconceptions as to what the elderly can do or like to do. And to my husband, Mandel for sharing with me his gentle patience and deeply inherent respect for individuals of all ages.

S.G.D.

NOTE: Portions of this book appeared in *Professional Nursing Home* and Geriatric Care and are used here with the permission of the editor, Mr. Ken Eymann.

CONTENTS

GERIATRIC
CONTENTMENT
A Guide to Its Achievement in
Your Home

Section One

I

INDIVIDUALIZE—DON'T GENERALIZE

THE TENDENCY TO TREAT most elderly people alike seems to be fairly common among young people. This may not always be justified. The elderly have had a lot of practice at becoming totally individual. Over the years, they have developed significantly different ways of reacting to specific situations. Their behavior patterns vary greatly, depending upon various habits they have acquired. Each of these people enters your home with an unusual intermingling of experiences and reactions peculiar to him alone. Many will very quickly find other residents with whom they have much in common. But we cannot expect them all to get along well with each other. It would be strange indeed if at least some did not find it hard to peacefully entwine their actions and thoughts with those of total strangers.

Working *with* their firmly entrenched habit patterns is most likely to bring peace and contentment to the majority of your residents. This can be most easily accomplished by trying to match like personalities when selecting roommates, table partners, etc. The insensitive or harried staff member might try to justify random selections with such rationalizations as "He couldn't get along with anybody," or "Our space is limited," or "People have to learn to make adjustments." There are times when one or all of these statements might be true. Nevertheless, one should still try every possible solution to a difficult situation. The resulting calm and professional fulfillment would be well worth the effort.

What should the procedure be when a new resident enters your home? Hopefully you will have already had the opportunity to talk with many people, including relatives, professionals, and the individual himself, about the type of person he is. From these conversations you will have been able to glean some of his likes and dislikes. Some obvious preferences can be determined at the outset. Does he enjoy bright sunlight or semidarkness, because of cataract operations, perhaps? Does he enjoy lots of fresh air or does he like a very warm room? Does he like to retire immediately after supper with the lights out or does he like to stay up in the evening to read, play games, watch television, or visit? Matching roommates according to their preferences for these simple but daily occurrences can prevent much unnecessary friction.

This is not meant to suggest, however, that residents of the same room need necessarily be alike in either physical or mental capabilities. In the same way that opposites sometimes attract in choosing a marriage partner, so it can be in this situation. Some ambulatory residents might derive great satisfaction from being needed by a roommate who is confined to bed. Another might conceivably be very content to have a roommate who does not converse at all or only when absolutely necessary.

One should explain to the new resident that the utmost care will be exercised in selecting a roommate with whom it is hoped he will be most comfortable. It should also be explained that sometimes circumstances make it necessary to make changes. These changes are only made when necessary for the maximum comfort of *all* of the residents concerned.

Obviously some traits may not be apparent when a resident first arrives at a facility. The answer, then, is a policy of flexibility. Upon gathering of sufficient evidence that roommates are not suited to one another, be prepared to make a careful move. This should only be done after considered analysis of the likes and dislikes of all residents involved. Even a move to a nearby room can be disturbing to some people. It is wise to apprise families of contemplated moves. They can often be very helpful in interpreting your motives to the resident. There will be times when moves are not popular with all of the parties directly or indirectly involved. Hopefully your sincere desire to do what is best for all concerned will help them to accept the inevitable until they are used to the change.

Similarly serious thought should be given to the assignment of dining room seats. Pleasant, or at least acceptable, company at meal time can contribute immeasurably to one's enjoyment of the food. Combine this with attractive centerpieces and a generally cheery atmosphere for at least three bright time slots in everybody's day!

Once the resident has been moved into his room, the aides who will be responsible for his care take over. It is good to remember that whenever possible one should sit down when talking to a resident, even for a minute. Then he knows that for that moment he really has your undivided attention, busy as you are. A brief but sincerely meant compliment about the resident's clothing, hair-do, etc. can make him feel very good, indeed.

Some residents may speak very slowly, or tend to ramble. Under the guise of being busy, we may thoughtlessly walk away while they are still talking. A painful feeling of rejection may be caused by such unintentional behavior. Every effort must be made not to do this, or at least to apologize when one must leave under such circumstances.

When speaking to one who is hard of hearing, stand or stoop to where he can see your lips. Get his attention before speaking. In a similarly thoughtful way, announce to a person with visual difficulties that you have arrived in his room. Also tell him when you are about to leave. Thus he will not be embarrassed because he is not aware of your presence! It is well to remember that in many elderly people more than one of their senses may be somewhat less acute than normal. While a youthful person with a visual impairment might feel your presence with the aid of a highly developed hearing ability, the older person might not have this advantage.

Sometimes in our sincere desire to appear professional and efficient we may neglect one of the most valuable sources of information and treatment guidance—the patient, himself.

When we find ourselves confronted with a patient for the first time, how do we proceed to care for him? Our eyes tell us at a glance certain basic facts. If he is in a wheelchair, we must learn the extent of the disability. In the ideal situation, you will have been fully informed by your supervisor or other staff member regarding each new resident you are to handle. For a variety of reasons, however, this does not always happen.

Whether you approach a new patient armed with adequate information or not, the following basic approach can be the beginning of a very satisfactory relationship for both of you. Even though you may be very pressed for time, try to allow a few extra minutes for your initial introduction. Speak your name clearly, give the patient the opportunity to repeat it, and say his full name with dignity and respect. Tell him you are going to care for him. As you approach each task, observe him carefully for signs of apprehension or discomfort. If the patient is unable to communicate with you verbally because of a physical or mental disability, you will have to rely on gentle trial and error to determine the best way to handle him. But as in the case of one severely arthritic patient, there was an easier way. It was a simple matter for her to tell the aides exactly how to move her from her wheelchair to the commode or bed with a minimum of discomfort to her. Her way also put a minimum of strain on the aides. Yet after nineteen years in several facilities, she could sadly relate numerous incidents in which the aides refused to listen to her. They ignored her suggestions, assuming and insisting they knew best how to do their job. The result was often unnecessary pain for the patient and resentment on the part of the staff members when she complained.

Treat each resident with the consideration and respect you expect from those around you. If the requests he makes for his care are unfeasible or unreasonable, you will of course have to explain your reasons for rejecting them. The average resident can accept this. Even if he doesn't agree, he will sense your sincerity and underlying concern.

II

STAFF MEETINGS AND
IN-SERVICE TRAINING

R EGULAR STAFF MEETINGS and in-service training sessions
can do much to improve personnel relationships and all
aspects of operating a good home.

This is the time and the place for all levels of employees
to share their concerns regarding the best resident care. If
the stage has been properly set, it will be a stimulating time
for mutual improvement.

Brief profiles of new residents should be given, and their
care and needs outlined. Questions can be asked regarding
the care of established residents. Solutions can be suggested
and agreed upon or discarded. Difficulties that have been en-
countered can be explained, and solutions explored together.

If the proper atmosphere of acceptance and understanding
has been created, even accidents or mistakes, simple or serious, can be discussed to the benefit of everyone. Suppose a
resident had been left out in the cool breezes too long, handled
too roughly, restrained too tightly, or not tightly enough. In
an atmosphere where blame and recrimination are the rule,
every effort will be made to conceal such happenings. If they
were discovered, no one would admit to having done them.
In a home where genuine concern for the resident is upper-
most and the staff maintains mutual respect for each other,
everyone feels secure in discussing such matters so that they
will not happen again. Certainly most accidents and discom-

fort occur through lack of knowledge or foresight, rather than wilfull neglect.

One simple way to avoid some difficulties is to make it a staff policy that each staff member finish what he starts. If he helps a resident to the toilet, he returns to help him back to his chair or bed. If he takes someone outdoors, he makes it a point to go out for him again after a reasonable period of time. Care must be taken not to expose one too long to the sun or to chilly winds.

It has been discovered that many residents hesitate to be taken from their rooms for any diversion because they are afraid of being forgotten. In the event that a staff member finds himself unable to return to the resident, it is his responsibility to have a fellow employee finish whatever task he started. In that case, the thoughtful stand-in will cheerfully say something like "Hi. Marg asked me to come for you because she will be delayed a few minutes. Are you ready to return to your room now?" Such a statement accomplishes two important things. His faith in Marg is retained because he knows she didn't forget him. He feels good because you asked if he is ready to return, showing respect for his judgment and his wishes.

The best possible care for all residents most assuredly requires maximum performance from all staff members. There are those administrators and supervisors who, in a misguided effort to retain sufficient help, feel compelled to ignore a certain amount of negligence on the part of employees. On the contrary, experience has proven that such a policy is likely to promote more discontent and turnover among the staff. Why? Because most of us really want to do our best. We want to be honestly proud of the job we are doing. Although our lazy streaks may come to the fore in a permissive situation, one comes to dislike, even hold in contempt, the person in authority who allows such a situation to prevail.

Even though the patient load is divided up and all staff members will not be involved in each case, a brief explanation of the condition of each new resident should be given to everybody. This may be done vocally or in writing. In the event that one is needed to assist in a different section temporarily, he will at least know something about the people in his care. Many times the alert staff member can apply what he learns regarding specialized care of one resident to the care of others. Equally important is the general atmosphere of the professional approach which derives from such discussions or memos. In those homes where such sessions are not held, or such information disseminated, employees may get the feeling that maybe no one really knows how to treat the resident, or even worse, that no one really cares.

A thoroughly distressed patient was once heard to remark, "How can that young whipper-snapper know how I feel? She's probably never had a good pain in her life!" When you stop to think about it, you will have to agree that she may very well be right. Many young people have known little if any physical discomfort. In staff meetings we can discuss the need to become acutely sensitive to the needs of the resident. Let us consider the situation in one nursing home where it was the custom to have each patient up and dressed by midmorning. They remained up until the approach of evening. In general, one would say that this is a commendable approach. It is fine for the residents who are well enough to enjoy the physical and mental stimulation this could afford them. But what about the resident who objects constantly, or doesn't feel well on a particular day? Staff members should feel free to discuss the situation with their immediate supervisor or to use their own judgment in an unusually stressful situation. One can certainly sympathize with a woman ninety-five-years old, and of completely sound mind, who expressed her resentment rather bitterly. She was furious that after successfully negotiating almost a century of education, travel, and responsible positions, she is now dependent upon these arrogant youths who pay no attention to her personal desires. Although they may think they are carrying out their jobs conscientiously, they are neglecting one very important aspect of good care. The feelings of the patient are never to be disregarded. Only the extremely naive and inexperienced would presume to suggest that all discontentment can be eliminated in this way. But certainly every effort should be made to interpret our actions and rules to the resident. There must never be any question in his mind that we have the utmost concern for his welfare and the utmost respect for his wishes. In the event that we really cannot in good conscience grant his wishes, at least let us make every effort to make it clear to him that we are not merely flaunting our authority but are looking out for his best interests.

A virtually untapped source of education for staffs of nursing homes and homes for the aged are the doctors whose patients reside there. Many would welcome an invitation to coffee or lunch, combined with the opportunity to explain a particular mental or physical condition and methods of treatment and approach considered most effective. The beneficial effects of involving outside professionals in your in-service training are twofold. Not only does your staff obtain valuable insight into the conditions of your residents, but the community is made aware of the high caliber of care you are providing.

Another valuable source of knowledge might very well be the experts on your own payroll. There are homes where the occupational therapy and physical therapy rooms are regarded primarily as places to park the resident while giving his room a thorough cleaning! By giving these therapists recognition as experts in their fields, you give them status in the eyes of employees who may not realize the extent or importance of therapist training. A staff which understands the methods and goals of therapeutic treatments can assist in interpreting them to the residents and their families. They may even subtly encourage self-help along these lines.

Most homes specializing in care of the aged must, of necessity, have a high proportion of untrained employees. This need not be bad for several reasons. First of all, if we are agreed that we are striving for a genuinely homelike atmosphere, then tender, loving care is paramount. There is no guarantee that the educated have more of this to give than the uneducated. Sometimes the opposite is true. There are those who make the mistake of adhering so closely to the book that not enough genuine feelings of kindness and warmth seep through. A sincere person who likes and understands older people can learn a great deal from on-the-job-training sessions and supervisory sessions, however brief or informal, but the fact remains that the ideal team must necessarily consist of the proper balance of skilled and unskilled employees. Each must have a thorough understanding and respect for the abilities and duties of the other. One can readily see how an aide might come to resent the higher pay given to a nurse or therapist if she did not understand the extent or importance of her training. The role of each staff member and how it complements the others should be carefully gone over for the benefit of all. Freedom from resentment of one employee against another leads to the type of harmonious relationships needed for warm interaction on all levels of care in the home.

III

LOVE THOSE FAMILIES AND FRIENDS!

A GOOD RECREATIONAL PROGRAM requires the assistance and cooperation of every staff member in your home, as well as that of many of the visitors. Fortunately this is a two-way street, since an effective pleasure-oriented social climate makes overall care a much easier task. The resident who is looking forward to a pleasant afternoon in handicraft class or at a birthday party is generally happy and cooperative. At least he is much more likely to be so than one who expects little or no change or excitement to take place this day or any other.

The average resident whose total life is now in our hands has either been an employed worker or a housewife. For some, this was many years ago; for others, it was quite recent, but most likely all have spent the major part of their lives making choices pertaining to their physical care and their emotional desires. Now they find themselves in a situation where not only are these major decisions no longer necessary, but even minor ones may not be solicited or even allowed. To find one's self in such a situation can be devastating to even a very stable personality.

The effect can be equally bad on the staff. How much easier it is for one to care for a resident who has activities in which he plans to take part. What is the incentive for finishing lunch within a reasonable time if there is nothing to do when the meal is done? Somehow the entire day takes on new meaning if there is something planned for part of it. Exercises or bathing must be accomplished in the morning, since there will not be time in the afternoon. Lunch must be finished on time to allow for a rest before the fun starts. Choices must be made as to what clothing one will wear. Let the resident make his own selections if he is able. This is an opportunity to boost his morale by showing him you respect his taste and his ability to make even minor decisions for himself. There is a reason for applying makeup or for shaving if one is going to a party or expecting company. There is an incentive for carefully combing one's hair and even using a dab of that birthday or Chirstmas gift cologne that is stashed away in the drawer.

One need not seek very far to find strong justification for including visiting families and friends in the social activities as much as possible. In many instances it can make the visit much more pleasant for all concerned. Some families suffer greatly from their decision to place the relative in a home, regardless of whether it was of necessity or of convenience. They are less apt to search for things about which they can complain if they see pleasant activities in progress in which even they are invited to participate.

If the person they are visiting happens to be confused or uncommunicative, frequent visiting can become tedious at best, or even unpleasant. If we can help these loyal, dedicated relatives and friends by providing a diversion they may enjoy seemingly even more than the resident, bravo! This is one more valid reason for having truly stimulating recreational activities in your home. Ultimately it contributes to the generally normal, happy atmosphere for which we are striving. The resident who appears to be very much out of things because of poor hearing, vision, or general depression, may amaze you with his obvious enjoyment of an activity which he attends with his family. Even the chronic complainer may never let you know how much he enjoys your programs until by accident you forget to come and get him one afternoon!

The uninitiated staff member may sometimes resent the presence of family or friends, and even consider them intruders. This is unfortunate and reasons should be explored. Of course, every effort should be made to accomplish basic custodial tasks and treatments in the morning before guests are apt to arrive, but the staff need feel no embarrassment if visitors come at unusual hours or at a difficult time. One need not hesitate to ask visitors to step out of the room when personal assistance might cause embarrassment to the resident, visitors, or staff. One should always remember to close the door when caring for a resident's intimate needs. We must respect their privacy, thereby helping them to maintain their dignity at all times.

Families and friends can do much to keep the resident contented by frequent friendly visits; by interpreting to him the need for certain treatments, medication and procedures, and by taking the resident out for exercise, fresh air, and a change of scenery. If the patient is not able to leave the home, he can be mentally removed temporarily from his limited surroundings by the introduction of bright new thoughts of the outside world. Stimulating discussions with loved ones may take his mind off himself and his daily routine. This can give him other things to think about, even including family problems. In fact, hearing about the difficulties his children are having raising their teen-agers might just make him appreciate being a senior citizen in these trying times!

Elderly people very much like to see children of all ages. Especially since some people are totally confined to the home, it should be the policy to welcome all such visitors. In the event that groups of children are coming to entertain or visit, one staff member should be designated to talk with them beforehand. He should explain briefly what the group is likely to encounter. He might explain that the appearance of some of the residents is unusual, and perhaps share with them some of the causes. He should also explain that some of the residents might behave in unusual ways, and encourage the children to give possible reasons, if they know any. He should then elaborate on their answers if necessary. He should remind them that friendly smiles and words of greeting make everybody feel loved, and how they will be especially appreciated by the people they have come to visit.

It is important to remember that to the resident, the staff and other residents of the home, plus his family and other visitors, if any, represent his entire world. He needs to feel that the staff likes and appreciates his family, and that the converse is true as well. Furhermore, when the staff lets the family know that they like the resident and understand him, the family feels better about his being there. They may be genuinely concerned about whether the patient is getting adequate care, and anything the staff can do to allay those fears is to everyone's benefit. Busy as they are, the staff should try to be available when needed to explain the patient's condition and ease the minds of concerned family members.

In the event that a resident should become very ill, a private emergency room should be available for him if he is not going to be removed to the hospital. Thus we can avoid upsetting the roommate and give the family the privacy they need at this time. If death appears imminent, a staff member equipped emotionally and through experience to handle the situation, should remain nearby. Families may vary in their reactions and these cannot be predicted, but we surely want to provide the maximum amount of compassionate and professional support at this time.

IV

RESIDENT ADVISORY BOARD

"IF I RAN MY BUSINESS as inefficiently as this place, I'd have been bankrupt the first year." Ever hear a statement like that from one of your residents? Did it ever occur to you that he might just be right? Right or not, wouldn't it be a good idea to at least listen to what he has to say? He might have some genuinely helpful suggestions, and it will certainly make him feel better if he is invited to express his feelings about whatever changes he feels should be made.

Instead of just encouraging him to sound off in front of anyone he can get to listen, why not organize a resident advisory board? It should be composed of people who are able to comment intelligently on any and all aspects of home activity, as well as ones who wish to be included. Do not be unduly concerned about attacks on your pet menus, staff members, or methods of operation. Plan to listen carefully and then utilize the opportunity to interpret staff reasons for functioning as they do. Furthermore, you may receive some suggestions which you will find worthy of adoption.

Frequently when we are in the midst of a situation for any length of time, we cease to evaluate our actions. Methods and procedures become routine, almost sacred. "We've always done it that way," is a common answer when one questions a particular procedure. That is precisely why it is wise to reconsider our approach when it is brought to our attention.

This brings to mind the case of a brilliant man who was the

19

victim of a diving accident at the age of ninteen. When I met him, he had been confined to a wheelchair for forty years. He was totally dependent upon those about him for all his needs. They even had to place his cigarettes in the holder designed especially for him by a loving relative. He had been in several nursing homes and had spent hours watching the comings and goings of hundreds of staff workers. Certainly a man like that would have observed both wise and wasteful ways of using manpower and materials. He even figured out such details as traffic patterns which he felt could be improved. He had determined more convenient spots for storage of clean linens and the deposits for soiled laundry.

What a mutually satisfying experience it could have been for the staff and for him had there been a council in which he could have shared his ideas. Perhaps some were not practical. There may have been many other disadvantages to his plans. The staff may have been governing their actions by other things occurring simultaneously of which he was not aware. Nevertheless, the important thing is that it makes a resident feel good to know that he is respected enough to be listened to. And just as important, he might certainly discover that the staff has sensible reasons, or at least necessary reasons, for doing things as they do.

It is so much easier to accept a person's actions when we know the reasons for them, even though we may not agree with them. A stimulating discussion should find the staff ready to change old patterns for new ones, or at least to try them, when they appear to be more efficient or sensible.

Of all the complaints most frequently heard in any home, certainly meals come in for their share of the limelight. One might think that only houswives get into the habit of preparing the same meals week after week. It takes only a bit of elementary research to discover that institutional cooks are even more susceptible to this human frailty than the average housewife.

She has reasons for serving the same dishes, of course, not

the least of which is cost. But even the most economical proteins such as ground meat, tuna, and cheese can be prepared in an exciting variety of ways. No one recipe can be expected to please everybody. That is precisely what makes cooking such a challenge. The head dietician or cook should allow herself at least one hour a week to ferret out new recipes she would like to try.

A few minutes spent visiting with the residents to determine their reactions to what has been served pays off handsomely in good feelings and information. But do not make the mistake of noticing and inquiring of only those who come to the dining room. The bedridden may have a totally different outlook on life in general and foods in particular! If a new dish is well received, it should be placed in the "use often" file. If not, it should be marked accordingly and set aside. A quick check of trays as they return to the kitchen, to see what has been left untouched, can be very revealing. Limit the use of any foods not eaten by the majority of your residents. If you expected something to go well and it did not, try it again later. It might get a warmer reception at another season or merely at some later date.

One sure way to generate good feelings among the residents is to give them the opportunity to suggest menus now and then. This can be done either verbally at resident council meetings or solicited in writing via your monthly newspaper. It is wise to state in advance that difficulty of preparation or prohibitive costs might preclude granting some requests, but that every effort will be made to follow through. One might think that the requests would all lean toward such fancy foods as steaks or lamb chops, but that is not necessarily true. In one home where suggestions were solicited, one resident expressed a longing for mashed potato patties, another for pot roast cooked on the stove, instead of in the oven. These were simple desires easily satisfied and enjoyed by all. And the cook acknowledged with a grin that she wondered why she hadn't thought of them herself! Maybe it's a good thing she didn't.

Everybody enjoyed the interchange of ideas and desires which brought about their eventual inclusion in the menu.

If you have an especially alert council, it might want to consider the ambitious project of compiling a cook book composed of favorite recipes and menus of the residents. It could become a treasured souvenir of international culinary art. It behooves us to remember that when the present generation of the elderly is no longer with us, we will note a significant change in our population makeup. The next generation was born primarily in this country and has precious little, if any, firsthand memories of the old country to share with us.

Resident councils might also be used advantageously for interpreting to the other residents the behavior of difficult and bewildering or bewildered patients. Consider the case of a man who had had a stroke in middle age. He was partially paralyzed and unable to speak. His mind was very sharp, as was his temper. As a daily occurrence, or even more often, the staff and residents alike were treated to the dubious pleasure of temper tantrums rarely outdone by even the most robust of the younger generation.

A normal initial reaction would be one of swift retaliation with similarly hateful behavior. A moment of reflection, however, brings one to the obvious conclusion that there must be some underlying reasons for such unpopular reactions from this patient to normal, everyday occurrences. One explanation might be an all-consuming need for love and attention. Such obnoxious behavior could not promote much love, but it would certainly provoke a great deal of attention! Apparently one who feels starved for even the slightest bit of recognition would gladly settle for any kind of attention. A speech doctor described the plight of an intelligent person who cannot talk as similar to being dropped into a foreign land where everyone speaks a different language.

A thoughtful discussion of this problem in a council meeting might well result in more than one interpretation as to the reasons for this type of behavior. It might also result in suggested experiments as to how to deal with the problem. Perhaps the residents feel that there is some merit in the idea that the need for affection is a factor. One could help them to agree to make it a point to treat this person in a more friendly manner in the future. Some might complain that it is difficult to be nice to one who is frequently unpleasant. The alert staff member sitting in on the council meeting would seize this opportunity to clarify the issue. Wouldn't it be interesting to see if by their considerateness they might help this resident to modify his demanding attitude? Perhaps the approach agreed upon might be one of kindness plus firmness on the part of the entire nursing home family. Selfish demands would no longer be catered to merely to maintain peace and quiet. The important thing here is that everybody's feelings would be dealt with openly, and solutions sought from which everybody could benefit.

One of the most beneficial results of all of this discussion would be the subtle realization on the part of each resident that "This staff really cares what happens to each of the people who lives here, including me!"

It would be a mistake to deduce from what has been said that the suggestion is being made that treatment be placed in the hands of residents rather than staff. A few hours spent eavesdropping with a cluster of residents in any home brings one to the immediate conclusion that resident *and* staff behavior is thoroughly scrutinized each day. Wouldn't it be wise to channel this energy with the benefit of staff insight and guidance? In other words, since we know residents discuss amongst themselves, at great length, everything that goes on in the home, shouldn't we try to make the discussions productive? If we can point out the good things about an unpopular resident, plus possible reasons for his unacceptable behavior, everybody stands to benefit.

V

VOLUNTEER OR RESIDENT—
WHO BENEFITS MORE?

"SOMETIMES I WONDER who benefits more from this program, the residents or I!" Have you ever heard that cheerful exclamation from a happy, satisfied volunteer? Any nursing home, whether privately or publicly sponsored, surely need never have any qualms about its right to ask for volunteers for a recreational therapy program. Even a paid staff of several people could not duplicate the wonderful diversity of stimulation and interest that can be offered through an adequate volunteer staff. By promoting the participation of a large number of qualified volunteers who can devote regular hours to the program, it is possible to involve a variety of personalities and talents it would surely be prohibitive to hire on a scheduled basis.

And what of the benefits that the volunteers themselves derive from their dedication to such a worthwhile endeavor. Their own lives are brightened in direct proportion to the amount of pleasure they can immediately see they are bringing to the residents. If the effects of their efforts should take longer to become evident, it is just that much more gratifying when it finally does happen.

Another important aspect to consider is the effect a truly adequate volunteer program can have upon the community at large. Many people have had almost no contact with nursing homes, or even with any elderly people other than those in their immediate family or circle of acquaintances. There are many misconceptions concerning their needs, behavior, and care. What better interpretation to the community could be asked for than that given through the eyes of a justly proud volunteer? He has so many interesting, inspiring tales to share about what goes on behind our walls, and his remarks are given credence because one knows he has nothing to gain from it personally; no reason to tell anything but the truth.

It is frequently possible to start this program by enlisting the cooperation of a women's group in a nearby church. Patients, friends and relatives who happen to be frequent visitors are another possibility. A friendly letter to the minister or leaders of the various church organizations may bring a response. Follow-up telephone calls may be required, with an offer to visit the groups to explain the program in detail. By answering questions, we can clear up misconceptions which might otherwise keep people away. Personal contact can be very persuasive, so do not hesitate to invite the assistance of visitors you notice in the building. Request space in the local newspapers and the publications of nearby churches. Make your needs known. There are such vast, untapped resources in the persons of housewives and retired men just waiting for an invitation to help, but be ready for them the first time they attend. It is essential that this program be under the direction of a competent person, preferably someone experienced in handling this type of program. Medical knowledge, recreational skills of many kinds, plus a feeling for public relations make up the ideal combination!

There is nothing more devastating to a volunteer than the feeling that his help is not needed, unless it is the feeling that he is not being appreciated. Most of them wouldn't express this feeling in words, even if asked. As a matter of fact, they might not even know themselves why the experience is not proving to be satisfying. So rather than try to analyze it, the volunteer in the poorly supervised setup just quietly "fades away," and the unsuspecting institution one day finds itself quite alone.

Now then, is it just a lot of buttering up and flattery which is required to hold the average volunteer? Well, I suppose not! As a matter of fact, that is about as bad as the neglect we mentioned earlier. What is needed, first of all, is a careful explanation to each person as to the type of patient he is likely to encounter and suggested ways to handle each. It is important, however, to make it clear that we trust his judgment and are merely setting up guideposts. Anyone who has worked with the elderly knows that one thing we can count on is their unpredictability. Their physical condition on a particular day can change their personalities radically. In other words, what we must do is build up the confidence of the volunteer so that he does not hesitate to approach a resident, and can handle a variety of situations. He must have some idea of the reactions he can expect from the patient.

He must also know that we respect his ability to deal with the patient in a helpful, effective way. Especially when the volunteer is new, we must be sure to make ourselves available to share his experiences following each session. He may have specific questions as to a patient's condition or reactions. He may merely wish to recount his experiences and be reassured that he acted in the best interests of the resident.

An attendance sheet should be kept readily available for record purposes. The volunteer will tend to be more reliable if he knows that we know when he comes and that we are relying upon him. In a short time he will come to realize that the patients are relying upon him, too, and then we have it made! Once the volunteer knows how important his job is, he isn't likely to disappoint the staff or the patients. Let him know that you appreciate as much advance notice as possible when absence is unavoidable. He is entitled to know that you feel his presence will be missed. Tell him so and tell him what temporary arrangements you were able to make, if any, to fill the gap.

A monthly meeting for the volunteer staff serves as a wonderful medium for further stimulation and informal education. Here volunteers can share their experiences and learn from one another, as well as from various professionals in the field. The attending physicians, the head nurse, the pyhsical therapist, the social worker, the local clergyman, all might each be invited to speak to the group as part of a series of lectures and discussions. Each has something special to offer in the way of understanding and working with any or all of the residents a volunteer might encounter. A portion of each session might be devoted to specific case studies. Here again, by making such an informal educational program available to the volunteer, we are showing him concretely that we consider his contribution extremely valuable and are willing to match his efforts with our own.

Once the volunteer has become acquainted with the home and has learned to function adequately with residents who quite readily accept the program, take the next step. Give him the challenging assignment of some additional residents who have shown no interest in the program thus far. Let me reiterate that not every resident has a need for or wants to take part in the recreational program. We do, however, want to make certain that he understands it and knows that he can take advantage of it if he does desire to do so. A good visual aid and a staff stimulant is a large chart listing the names of all residents. Beside each name leave space in which the volunteer or therapist can insert the correct colored star which indicates the results of that week's or month's efforts. For example, one might designate a red star for a conversational visit, a blue star for a bedside activity, and a green star for attendance at a group function. Such concrete evidence of the degree of our success presents a challenge to everyone to continue to broaden his efforts.

If your home prints a newspaper, reserve a space for listing and thanking the volunteers each month. Once a year they should be honored at a gathering and each one presented with a certificate of merit. There is no substitute for a well rounded, well supervised, smoothly operating volunteer staff. Show your appreciation in the ways mentioned, and their enthusiasm and loyalty will prove boundless!

Section Two

VI

YOUR MONTHLY PUBLICATION

A MONTHLY PUBLICATION can be a delightful tonic. Properly executed, it will radiate warm feelings of enthusiasm and understanding to four elements essential to our operation —the residents, families and friends, the staff, and the community at large.

Your newspaper can educate, inform, involve, and entertain all of the people who come in contact with your organization. How much it does for each of these goals can vary each month, depending upon your immediate needs.

Even the most thorough intake procedure may leave certain questions unanswered, or the family may not remember all that was covered. A newspaper can be used to acquaint families and other interested parties with your policies, services, and facilities, such as beauty shop, laundry, etc. It can explain reasons for such rules as visiting hours or restructions on types of foods that can be brought in, if any. Much resistance can be broken down when rules are properly explained. The larger the home, the less likely it is that individual explanations can always be made. Your newspaper can do some of this for you; and just as important, whether the home is large or small, many people can accept this impersonal approach much more readily.

You can use your newspaper to share with families and residents many behind-the-scenes activities, such as the way menus are determined, the way roommates are chosen, the amount of laundry handled in a week, and techniques for keeping things mended and properly separated. The sensitive editor and administrator can feel those areas in which interpretation is needed.

Highlights of your monthly staff meetings can be shared with your readers. Wouldn't your families feel good to know that your staff is kept abreast of the latest treatment techniques? Shouldn't they be made aware that staff members are awarded a certificate for attending required in-service training sessions, if such is the case?

In a wisely used question and answer column one can set families' minds at ease regarding common anxieties many relatives experience when their relatives are in a home. For example, in a column entitled "Have You Been Wondering?" could be printed the following: "Sometimes I wonder how much my mother appreciates my visits. She seems so apathetic at times, or else she spends the entire time complaining about things I don't do, or don't do right."

Reply: You have no idea how much even a short visit means to your loved one. She listens eagerly for your familiar footsteps and talks about your visit long after you've left. It's easy to fall into a pattern of complaining to a captive audience, but try to overlook it. Talk about things of interest outside the home. Deep down she values your love and attention very much, but assumes you know it, and forgets to say so.

Notice that no attempt was made to use technical language. On the contrary, the entire column is couched in simple terms which can easily be understood by everyone.

If you have been successful in building up a good volunteer program or would like to do so, your newssheet can be an ideal aid. Advertise your needs. Give your volunteers well-earned recognition and express your appreciation. List their names and affiliations each month, being very careful not to forget anyone.

Printing staff and resident profiles is an effective way of

introducing new as well as old faces. Ideally, interviews can be conducted by resident reporters, who can also be used in other capacities. They can gather news, write columns, and keep a sharp eye out for jokes, poetry and cartoons which they think the readers might enjoy. Encourage original art work, too.

You will want to list resident birthdays each month as well as any special events scheduled for the near future. Current needs of the craft program can be solicited, such as empty juice cans, cigar boxes, discarded nylon hosiery, etc.

A most exciting aspect of your publication can be the monthly contests. Obviously, the first one should be to name the paper! Awarding the prizes can be a gala event shared by all, perhaps at the monthly birthday party. Another contest might be a personality quiz. In this one you list identifying true facts about residents and staff, such as "1. A former opera singer, 2. Beauty contest runner-up, 3. Mother of twelve children," etc. The winners are the ones who discover which of your residents and staff members fits each of the descriptions. This type of contest is especially good because it requires the contestants to ask questions of many people to ferret out the answers. New mutual respect and sometimes even lasting friendships have resulted from these contacts.

As a holiday approaches, one might choose a phrase such as Halloween Fun, Keep Smiling, or Happy New Year, and award a prize or several for the longest lists of words which can be made from the letters in the phrase.

Game tournaments, including checkers, Scrabble®, dominoes, and chess, can be announced in your paper. Bed patients can be encouraged to participate by assigning ambulatory residents or volunteers to play the games with them at their beside. Small engraved trophies make wonderful prizes for this type of contest. They can be obtained quite inexpensively in many so-called "'dime" stores.

Even with a large variety of monthly contests, one might not be able to stimulate the participation and interest of all

the mentally alert residents. But there is one way to include everyone, and that is by inviting folks to answer an interesting question. For example, "What is your advice to a high school graduate just starting out on his own?" To get the biggest response it would be wise to assign a staff, volunteer, or resident reporter to circulate in the building and write down everybody's answer. You can be certain that these pearls of wisdom will be sometimes amusing, sometimes amazing, and frequently quite revealing!

The question will come up as to whether or not staff should be allowed to participate in the contests. By all means, this is to be encouraged, since it is one subtle way of telling the residents that they are not isolated in a world of their own. It implies, and rightly so, that they are part of the total normal community of young and old, well and not-so-well, with interests and abilities on a par with all.

Even if you have your own duplicating machines in your offices, you might want to consider the new instant printing services to produce your paper. They are to be highly recommended, especially since they make creation of the original copy so easy. Articles can be typed individually, then cut out and glued on the pages wherever they fit and look best. Titles and simple drawings can be done with an ordinary pencil or marker. Once the headings have been carefully drawn or assembled from magazine letters, they can be cut out and pasted on the new issue each month. When you bring your pasted-together copy to the printer, he merely photographs each page and then prints as many as you need. There are no lines on the paper to reveal your secret of the patchwork technique.

Varying the color of paper used each month will help your readers identify new issues. The entire process of photographing and printing takes only about twenty minutes, and the cost is extremely nominal. If this service is not offered in your town, you can probably mail your original to a nearby city and have it ready for distribution in a few days.

If you do not already have one, do choose a publication

date and start the wheels turning for your first newspaper. By mailing a copy to those families who may not be frequent visitors you can maintain a continuing and valuable contact with them. The talent and enthusiasm you will uncover with your publication will prove rewarding to all who come in contact with your home.

VII

A BAKING AND GARDEN SALE

THE WAY TO ANYBODY'S HEART is through good food. And what could be better than freshly baked bread, rolls, and coffee cakes prepared by your residents for a bake sale?

Difficult? Not with a bit of advanced planning, Fun? Immeasureably so, for a larger number of volunteers, residents, and visitors than you might guess.

Stimulating enthusiasm for this project will most assuredly reveal personality traits in some residents that you may not have noticed before. Try not to forget to invite every resident to participate unless you know he is totally incapacitated. Men and women who show no interest in any other activity will astound you with their eagerness to join in. Here at last is something to do that is genuinely useful, worthwhile, and certainly cannot be classed as "kindershpiel" or child's play. In addition to that, a wonderful variety of physical and mental disabilities lend themselves to doing this with no problem. The little lady who took to eating the raw dough in one home was just as happy when offered maraschino cherries instead, and she was so glad to be included in the excitement of the day. And who knows what hostilities were worked out by the Finnish lady who spoke no English, but certainly proved that pounding and kneading bread dough is done the same way in any country!

How does one go about preparing for a genuine home (for the elderly, that is!) bake sale? First of all it is of prime importance to take members of the kitchen staff into your confidence. Ask them to help you select a baking date at a time when they are planning a simple evening meal. Then your use of the ovens will cause them a minimum of inconvenience. Your actual preparation of the breads can be done in the dining room, where there will be adequate table space for the maximum number of residents and volunteers to take part in the project.

There is no need to mix your dough unless you really want to, since the frozen product is ideal for the purpose. Excellent results were obtained at one nursing home with the frozen bread dough that comes packaged in three or five one-pound loaves. Ten residents with varying degrees of limitations, physical and mental, with the help of two volunteers and one therapist, were able to prepare forty-two pans for baking in three hours. Using this information as a guide, purchase the amount of dough you expect to use.

Have it laid out for defrosting on floured cloths, covered, six to eight hours before you plan to use it. The kitchen staff may be willing to do this for you when they arrive early in the morning. An added advantage to the frozen product is the fact that each piece weighs exactly one pound, so each of your customers will obtain full value for his money. Your residents will find the selling easy, and great fun, especially since they know they are offering an excellent product which the buyer will enjoy for two reasons: (1) It tastes good. (2) He's helping the home to provide a worthwhile project for the residents.

This project provides two days of fun and enjoyment—the day of preparation and baking, and the next day, reserved for selling, if there is any left! It is nice to hold the sale in a room where coffee can be served. Some customers will want to sample their purchases at once and share them with residents they may be visiting. One home found it had only a small portion of its delicacies left for the next day's sale because residents and staff bought things up as fast as they came out of the oven. Three varieties which have proved to be popular are what we called tidbit coffee cakes, onion snacks, and sesame bread twists. You are welcome to use the names!

The coffee cakes are made by cutting each pound loaf into small pieces, dipping them into melted butter, then cinnamon and sugar, and placing them in a greased pan. interspersed with maraschino cherries which have been rinsed and cut in half. Notice how some residents will space the cherries with precision-like accuracy; whereas others will enjoy tossing them in helter-skelter. The end product will be the same— scrumptious.

Prepare the onion snacks by cutting the dough into small pieces, dipping them into melted butter, then scattering them with frozen chopped onion in a greased pan.

For the bread twists, cut the loaves into three long pieces, stopping about one inch short of one end. Braid, pinch the loose ends together, and place in a greased loaf pan or cookie sheet. Brush the tops with an egg yolk mixed with two table-spoons of cold water, and sprinkle with sesame seeds. It is advisable to use aluminum foil pans in which you can sell your products just as they come from the oven. This simplifies packaging for sale and cuts down on dishwashing and kitchen clutter. Let the cut, arranged dough rise for a second time for forty-five minutes to an hour. Bake at 350° for about thirty minutes, until golden brown.

Your local newspaper will probably be very eager to cover this activity. Try to give them plenty of advance notice so they can give you adequate coverage. They may want to print pictures of the event for all to enjoy. Thus there can be much vicarious enjoyment for people who are so frequently saddened by the more usual type of nursing home publicity.

You will find it wise to start recruiting volunteer assistance in plenty of time. Many more residents can take part if they have sufficient help. For example, even the patient with partial paralysis of one or both arms can dip pieces of dough into the proper bowls and greased pans if the pieces are cut for him and everything is placed within easy reach.

Now that you have alerted the kitchen, lined up your volunteer help, ordered the necessary supplies, stimulated the interest of the staff and residents, and laid the ground work for your publicity, you're ready to have fun. You are sure to work your way into many a man's heart, and woman's, too!

If your bake sale happens to be a summertime venture, you might want to include with it some of the produce from your resident gardening project. Seeing things grow brings joy to the eyes of many people of all ages and stages of life. It seems to be especially meaningful to those who may have done some gardening or farming at one time during their more active periods. To those who have never been exposed to it, it can be a source of new-found pleasure and interest. Think of the fun of serving on your trays a salad made up of tomatoes, radishes, and greens planted and tended by your residents. If you don't have enough to sell with your baked goods, display some of the nicest produce. It's good public relations, and occasions button-popping pride on the part of those residents who tended and nurtured them to maturity.

Your resident gardening need not be limited to edibles, either. Imagine the justifiable pride when incoming visitors comment on the beauty of your flower beds weeded regularly by some of your residents. Don't make the mistake of assuming that what seems tedious and boring to you affects others that way, too. To the nature lover with time on his hands weeding can be stimulating and creative. In one home, gardeners were thoughtfully protected from the sun by large-brimmed gingham bonnets sewn by the handicraft group. Thus were two admirable projects entwined to everybody's mutual satisfaction.

VIII

A RIP-ROARING WHEELCHAIR OLYMPICS

"BY GOLLY, there's a bit of life in this old geezer yet!" Rex said. "Imagine a one-armed, stiff-legged old codger like me winning all these ribbons. I feel like a Christmas tree."

"Humph, you look like one, too," growled George, his roommate, who had been away for the afternoon. "Did everybody get a slew of ribbons like that?"

"I guess not," Rex said, raising his chest a bit higher. "Most everybody won at least one, though. Won't those people from the other homes have something to crow about and show off when they get back? You'd better stay around for the next Olympics, George, or are you afraid I'll put you to shame?"

"You, put me to shame? When's the next one going to take place? You can bet I'll be here to show you a thing or two!"

That spirited conversation was overheard following a very successful Wheelchair Olympics. You can have one, too, with a minimum of preparation and equipment. The amount of participation by your residents and visitors will surely justify the effort put forth.

Healthy competition can be friendly and stimulating at any age. This is just as true for the aged and handicapped as for any other group. The spirit and enthusiasm that will be in evidence during and after the games will last for days.

To make it even more exciting, send notes to nearby nursing homes and/or homes for the aged inviting them to send contestants to a Wheelchair Olympics. In order to keep the competition fair, specify that any and all participants must be in a wheelchair while taking part in the games. Anyone not confined to a wheelchair by necessity may borrow one for the events if he wishes to compete. Of course all visiting residents must be accompanied by an adequate staff complement from their own homes.

While you are awaiting answers to your invitations, your residents can begin preparations for the pending affair. First of all you will want to make prize ribbons for the winners of each game. Decide upon the color for each place, such as blue—1st place, red—2nd place, and white—3rd place. An attractive flower pattern can be cut from cardboard, and the residents can use it to duplicate many more on construction paper. Identify each one as to first, second, or third place with a magic marker, then staple the appropriately colored ribbon to it.

Please don't stint on the size of the flowers or the width of the ribbons. They decorate the proud winners beautifully, and why not? Be sure to make extra badges for each category, as there may very well be many ties. I hope so. When you see the faces brighten as badges are pinned in place, you'll know why we urge you to have lots of winners.

Your residents can also help assemble the props for some of the games. But don't reveal all of your plans to them. They will enjoy the additional fun of some surprises, too. The possibilities for games are many. Following are some that have proved to be popular:

1. *Penny Toss.* Float a small sauce dish in a basin of water. Place basin on the floor (or ground, if outdoors) in front of each contestant. Give him five pennies to toss into the sauce dish. Score only those pennies which remain in the dish.

2. *Bean Bags.* On stiff cardboard make a clown face with large holes for eyes, nose, mouth, and ears. Allow two points each time a bag (made by one of your residents, of course) is tossed through a hole. Stand the board

two feet away from each contestant. Give him three bags to throw. Record his score.

3. *Guessing Game.* Have each contestant guess the number of macaroni shells in a jar.

4. *Airplane Race.* At a craft session prior to the date of the Olympics have squadrons of paper planes made in different colors. Use a different color for each home. The team whose planes go the farthest wins. Since entire teams will win ribbons, it is thus possible for even the least adept to come away with at least one decoration.

5. *Backwards Race.* Let each contestant choose a visitor or staff member to run a backwards race for him. To add to the hilarity, have long strips of ribbons prepared to tie around the waist of each runner. Thus each resident can keep a tight rein on his "horse" as he runs for him!

Many of your visitors and volunteers will enjoy acting as monitors and scorekeepers. Take a few minutes beforehand to coach them as to the rules of each game. Caution them against the natural temptation to "bend" the rules for any particular participants unless it is really necessary. Genuine kindness would be the motivation, of course, but other contestants might resent it. Unhappy complaints of favoritism or laxity on the part of the "officials" can readily be avoided by complete fairness and adherence to the rules.

After the games and awards, something special in the way of refreshments would certainly be in order. If weather permits, and you are holding the event out of doors, a watermelon "feed" is fun. Actually anything which you do not regularly serve would add to the festive feeling of the day.

The awarding of the winning ribbons should be done with much flourish and fanfare. Try to allow enough time for the recipients to say a few words. Be prepared, though, for such totally unexpected comments as, "I never knew how much fun it could be living in a nursing home until I became an inmate here recently!" The gentle suggestion by the director that "resident" might be a better word went completely unnoticed.

Said "inmate," otherwise known as Rex to his friends, now keeps his winning ribbons neatly strung across the foot of his bed. Let the spirit of friendly competition and the gaiety of brightly colored ribbons add to the atmosphere and decorations of your home very soon.

IX

OLD-TIME PICTURE DISPLAY AND CONTEST

H AVE YOU EVER WONDERED what some of your residents and staff were like when they were younger? In some instances it is easy to surmise. In others, it might be very difficult to imagine what type of image their appearance and style conveyed. Seeing pictures from former days can sometimes give you many clues, unless it's a baby picture, and then you are out of luck! Any pictures can certainly be the source of much fun and conversation.

Post an attractive, eye-catching sign on your bulletin board announcing a new display. The poster should say that pictures of staff and residents taken at least twenty years ago are requested to be submitted to the office by a specific date. Each photo is to be identified with the year taken and the name of the resident or staff member clearly stated on the back. There are to be absolutely no identifying clues on the front. Each picture should then be given a number. The list of names and corresponding numbers should be kept up to date in the office by the person who accepts the pictures.

A small committee should be selected to mount the pictures in the lobby, keeping the names in absolute secrecy, but placing the number below each one. Although the home cannot be held responsible for the safe return of the pictures (this must be stated in advance), certainly every precaution should be taken to protect them. It is best to place them out of reach, or behind a glass or heavy plastic protective shield. A colorful border and colorful three-dimensional flowers or butterflies interspersed between the pictures add to the beauty of the display.

Did you notice that in the opening sentence of this chapter residents *and* staff were mentioned? By including staff in such a project as this we again demonstrate to the residents in very concrete terms that we do not consider them to be part of an isolated group. Seeing a staff member as he used to be can be just as astonishing as a picture of anyone else we haven't known for very long. Not only are we willing to risk laughing at ourselves publicily, then, but we are inviting the residents to laugh with us. That can be a real tonic.

By our willingness to share this bit of our personal lives with the residents we attest further to an awareness of their interest in the world around them. In other words, we make them one of us and figuratively lift them out of their limited world at least for a little while.

When the final date approaches for submitting pictures for the display, distribute sheets of paper with numbers and lines corresponding to the numbers of the photographs that have been entered and posted on your display. Set a date for the close of the contest, at which time the sheets with the names filled in must be returned at the culminating party.

Try to help as many of the entrants as possible to attend the party. With a great deal of pomp and ceremony, and a little music, return each photo to its owner, thereby revealing its true origin. Invite those who are able, to state briefly the circumstances surrounding the taking of the picture. In this way you are taking advantage of one more opportunity to give status and recognition to residents and staff alike.

While the party is in progress, one person should be quietly checking the contest entries which were collected as people entered the room. The one who has the best "I.Q." (Identification Quotient!) gets top prize, the one with the least gets a booby prize, and it's fun to give a few more prizes, too. Have several on hand, keeping in mind that they can't all be candy, since some winners may be diabetic. Plants make nice gifts, as do jewelry, toilet articles, or reading and writing material.

Close the party with a song or two, some cookies, and a hot cup of coffee. The warm feelings engendered will not be limited to the abdominal region, of that you can be sure!

X

HEART-OF-GOLD AWARD

I T IS NICE TO BE TOLD that you have a heart of gold, and even nicer if you can wear one to prove it! Such is the case in homes which have adopted the custom of awarding a "Heart of Gold" pin each month to a deserving resident. Candidates for the award are those who have been seen frequently being helpful to fellow residents.

Once you have decided to embark upon the program, the steps follow in a logical sequence. Place a colorful, attractive sign in a prominent place in the lobby, encouraging residents, visitors, and staff to recommend award candidates. Recommendations should be made in writing, if possible. Final selection is made by the administrator and an informal committee of his choice.

There are probably as many reasons for choosing the winner as there are residents in your home, and all of them equally good. One ambulatory resident may delight in assisting wheelchair patients to the dining room or lounge. Another may make it a point to visit frequently with a bed patient who has no family or friends in town. Perhaps there is a resident who likes to assist the aides with bed-making in the morning. And how about the terminal cancer patient who has a word of encouragement for everyone who stops by to cheer *her* up? Or the multiple sclerosis patient who keeps everybody laughing with his terrific sense of humor? See what I mean? You'll have no trouble selecting one person each month deserving of the honor.

But I would like to suggest that you be bold, and now and then select one who may *not* seem to deserve it, at least not to the casual eye. Have you ever talked to a fellow staff member and discovered to your surprise that he found a particular resident sweet and pleasant, while to you he always seems irritable? There could be many reasons for this. Perhaps your particular role in the home calls for providing services which he resents. Perhaps you got off on the wrong foot with him or your personalities differ radically. Maybe he is very unhappy for a reason which has nothing to do with you. Whatever the reason, maybe we can give him cause to change his behavior by praising his brighter side, which someone has already witnessed. Even if we haven't really seen much evidence of its existence, we could have confidence that it lies dormant, just awaiting proper encouragement before it blossoms forth.

Equally important as the giving of the award itself is the manner of presentation. The well-prepared administrator will carefully highlight the recipient's many fine points. He will no doubt mention qualities and services of which many fellow residents and staff members had not been aware. The presentation speech should be carefully thought out beforehand. It should focus upon all of the resident's good points. Even personality traits which we so often take for granted, such as cheerfulness upon awakening in the morning or a ready smile to newcomers, can be mentioned. You will find that many of your residents will adopt these traits after they have been brought to their attention. This presentation speech should also be printed in your monthly newsletter for the benefit of those who could not be present when the award was made. Having it in writing will serve as an additional reminder and guide to residents who may be aspiring to be the recipient of the award at some future date.

Occasionally there may be complaints from a staff member or resident as to the wisdom of a particular choice for the honor. One should use this opportunity to share the reasons for the selection. He should also elaborate upon the basic philosophy behind the Heart of Gold Award. One can explain to the trusted staff member or resident the idea that at times we hope to encourage the development of a happier resident by means of the presentation. Sometimes a patient's behavior changes markedly once he knows that we *expect* kindness, cheerfulness, and even general assistance from him.

Some residents may have become so accustomed to depending upon others for their own needs that it might not occur to them to help others a little less fortunate than themselves. Some might be indulging in temporary self-pity as a result of having recently left private dwellings to live in this less independent environment. Discussions about the Heart of Gold Award might very well help them to feel less concern about themselves and more for others.

In discussing the award and its recipients with residents, it is well to point out that making the selection each month is usually very difficult, since so many are worthy of the honor. One never knows when his turn might come up.

Locating heart-shaped pins may be easier around Valentine's Day and other holidays, such as Mother's Day and Christmas. It is wise to purchase a dozen or so when you locate some. Colored stones add to the beauty and are not objectionable to the men when worn as lapel pins, either. Prices range from fifty cents up, so budgetary limitations need not restrict your use of this stimulating technique.

A cherished decorator item in your lobby or main lounge might well be a Heart of Gold Award plaque. Instruct a local artisan to prepare a stained wood background on which to mount a gold heart fashioned from copper or brass. You may then send it out periodically to be engraved or imprinted with the names and dates of those who receive the Heart of Gold Award pin each month.

XI

BIRTHDAY FUN

FORTUNATELY FEW OF US can resist an excuse for a party, and certainly birthdays are no exception. They give us the opportunity to involve many residents personally while everybody joins in the fun.

Early in the month a poster should be prominently placed in the lobby so everybody can reserve the date. The wording might be something like this:

YOU ARE INVITED
to our monthly
BIRTHDAY CELEBRATION
Wed., Oct. 22, at 2:00 P.M.
RELATIVES AND FRIENDS ALWAYS WELCOME!

Dress up your sign with flowers or birthday symbols that are hand-drawn with crayons or paints, or simply cut out of magazines. If you have not been in the habit of keeping a monthly calendar which indicates which of your residents have birthdays coming up in the next month, this is a good time to begin. Each one should receive a birthday card from the home on the proper day, since the party may not fall on his date. When the day of the party arrives, it is wise to alert all staff members as to who is to be honored that day. The names should be announced over the loud speaker, or personally. This must be done immediately after lunch to allow the nursing staff sufficient time to prepare those residents who may need help. Some will require a short nap after lunch in order to enjoy the party to the fullest.

Attractive birthday crowns should be prepared to be presented to each celebrant. They need not be elaborate, but colorful. Any 8½″ by 11″ paper can be used, cut in half lengthwise in zigzags or scallops, thereby making two crown fronts from each sheet of paper. Designs or flowers can be drawn on with crayons or paints. Narrow strips of paper can be stapled to the back to make the crowns complete. Some of your residents might enjoy preparing these crowns during a craft session earlier in the month. One can really get fancy with a bit of glue, glitter, and imagination!

After lunch make it a point to visit the room of each birthday celebrant to show him his crown, and personally invite him to the party. If he is reluctant to attend, your offer to stop by for him might make him feel more secure. If he cannot or will not attend, place the crown upon his head or upon his bedside table and tell him you will return with some birthday cake later. Do not fail to keep your promise.

Be sure to include the kitchen staff in your plans for the party, so they can prepare some refreshments. It will make some additional work for them, so they should have sufficient notice. Besides a sheet cake or cookies to be served to everyone, it is nice to have a small traditional birthday cake. Some places make this the kind of cake that can later be served to the diabetics. Since most homes feel it is unsafe to light the candles, it is wise to have some other decorations on the cake, too, such as candy or artifical flowers. Try to arrange to have an instant camera on hand. This can be used to take a picture of each proud wearer of the birthday crown, after you have placed the birthday cake on the table in front of him. The picture is his, of course, to show to friends and relatives who may have not been able to attend the party. He will cherish it as a remembrance for a long time.

Try to have song sheets available which are double spaced and have fairly large print. It is good to have the songs numbered so they can be located more easily. Any instrumental accompaniment helps to stimulate participation, but good community singing can also be done without such help. Encourage residents and guests to request their favorite tunes, and do not be shy about asking them to assist you if you do not know the tune. In this subtle way you may be pleasantly surprised to discover that one of your residents was a choir member or even an opera singer. If you listen closely, you may hear someone naturally harmonizing. This might even be the beginning of an improptu barber shop quartet! Since it takes most people a few minutes to recall the tune and the rhythm of a song, it is usually wise to sing each song through twice, if it is to be fully enjoyed. One little French woman who spoke no English became positively radiant when "Alouette" was sung in French, then Hebrew and English. It was the first time many of the people who had known her for some time had heard her voice at all.

After about twenty minutes of singing, invite some of the residents to dance with you. A simple waltz, two-step, or fox-trot makes a good beginning. Save the fast numbers for a little later, when you know who your dancers are! Hadn't thought of the elderly and even the sick as potential dancers? Don't eliminate anybody from your list of invitations unless you think their doctors or families might have reason to object. You will discover that even patients who have difficulty walking may still enjoy dancing. The rhythm of the music often seems to relax tense muscles, and they move much more freely on the dance floor. It has been my experience that those who are not able or do not wish to dance derive a great deal of pleasure from watching others do so. One unpleasant spinister who had been fighting constantly with the other residents heard her first kind words from them after she had danced several numbers with the therapist. The residents were astounded at her ability to keep time to the music, and many stopped to compliment her as they passed her in the halls. Thereafter she eagerly awaited each party, anticipating the opportunity to dance again and glean a bit of recognition which she so sadly lacked.

Just prior to refreshment time, recognition should be given to each of the birthday celebrants individually. One at a time, those wearing the birthday crowns should be introduced by name. Most of them will be proud to divulge their ages and receive an admiring round of applause. If one forgets, relatives or friends can usually be of help. A question such as, "What birthday do you recall as having been the most exciting in your life?" may bring some touching or amusing replies. For example, one resident, with tears in her eyes, replied, "This one. It's the only birthday party I've ever had!"

Be sure not to slight any of the people who are wearing crowns. Even those who appear to be quite confused may amaze you with their answers. If you have created an atmosphere of warmth and congeniality by your manner, relatives will not be embarrassed if answers are not quite in keeping with the question. With your genuine warmth and respect to guide you, and a bit of practice thinking on your feet, you will be able to gracefully rephrase inappropriate answers or cover up with a kind comment. After you have spoken to each one of the people wearing crowns, lead everybody in the singing of "Happy Birthday," substituting the words "dear friends" for individual names. You may find it fun to add the following verse:

> May you live to be a hundred,
> May you live to be a hundred,
> May you live to be a hundred,
> And then a hundred more!

Start to serve the refreshments while someone is taking the birthday remembrance pictures discussed earlier.

Encourage residents and guests to help with passing out and collecting song sheets, and serving the refreshments. We all feel better when we are doing something useful. We need to be needed by others. It is wise to assign one staff member to serve the diabetics their special refreshments among the first. That way guests will not unwittingly serve them something they shouldn't have.

Return patients to their rooms following the party so they can relax before supper. If you have promised to look after certain residents whom you brought down, don't go back on your word. It is perfectly all right to allow a thoughtful visitor to take over for you as long as you explain it to the patient, and he doesn't object. That way he is more likely to accept your invitation to join in the festivities again soon.

XII

YOUR OWN VAUDEVILLE SHOW

IF YOU HAPPEN TO HAVE among your constituents many fairly able people, consider producing your own stage show. Few activities will surpass this one in generating so much wholesome excitement and fun. And it provides the maximum opportunity for involving residents with a wide variety of talents and interests.

Since many of the participants may find it difficult to commit parts to memory, try to avoid the necessity for learning lines. This can most easily be done by using a script which is composed of short, descriptive narrations. These can be presented by one or two narrators placed to one or both sides of the stage area.

Writing of the script can be done by a resident or a staff member. Ideally it should be about a subject in which your residents have a particular interest. However, if no such subject presents itself, there are many of universal appeal that one can draw upon.

Once the theme for the presentation has been decided, the type of stage action must be selected. Singing and dancing lend themselves especially well to this type of presentation and cast, as do simple pantomimes. By using large groups in each number, one can fit in even those with much more enthusiasm than talent!

One such performance given by a Golden Age Club revolved around a series of recollections of an imaginary member celebrating her eighty-fifth birthday. She was the narrator. The show began with a medly of her favorite tunes played by a volunteer orchestra. (In some cities the local musicians' union may provide the players.) The spotlight was then focused upon the woman who was celebrating her birthday. She stood comfortably before the lecturn and microphone reading from the script. This part could just as easily be played by one who is in a wheelchair. She describes her delight at being able to celebrate with so many good friends. She realizes that as she thinks back upon her life, the most important events that took place seemed to be associated with, or described by one of her favorite songs. Perhaps the group you are working with happens to be composed of primarily one particular ethnic group. If so, the script should ideally include some of their favorite songs, maybe even in a foreign language. In any case, you will also want to include selections from our rich American heritage of folk and popular songs of the past hundred years or so.

After the script has been written weaving together the events you wish to highlight in your show, plan the rehearsals. Four to six weeks is ideal. Much more than that may result in a lack of enthusiasm and even boredom. Songs and dances should be learned during short sessions, preferably with musical accompaniment. In many cases the voices of the elderly may not be strong or even melodic. But what they may lack in tonal quality can be easily overshadowed by their inherent charm and enthusiasm. In any event, instrumental support can help tremendously. Should you be so fortunate as to have someone with a good voice in the group, by all means use him as a soloist with a chorus. Do not hesitate to include in your chorus any and all residents who wish to participate in the show. The more the merrier, with or without the best singing voices. The only absolute requirement is a ready smile (even that can ge dispensed with if necessary!) and the willingness to do as the group does in getting on and off stage, making costume changes, etc.

Simple little dances should be an integral part of the program if at all possible, as they liven things up considerably. Should your group already know some folk dances they would enjoy doing, by all means use them. If not, anyone in your home who is at all adept at dancing can make up easy steps to the songs you plan to present. For example, partners can waltz or two-step in a circle, then place hands on shoulders in a large circle and glide to each side; take hands and step to the center of the circle, and then out; then waltz around again. A little imagination will go a long way here. Do not feel bound to have men as partners for each of the women. The proportion is rarely even, and women dance as well, if not better sometimes, with female partners.

Certainly no show is really complete without costuming, and a show presented by the elderly is no exception. Using a basic outfit, with additions for each number, is a good technique for many reasons. It is inexpensive. The costume changes can be accomplished with a minimum of effort. There is less cutting and fitting to do.

An example of a good basic costume is white blouses and black skirts for the women, white shirts and black trousers for the men. If you are located in a fairly large city and really want to go all out, try to arrange rental of a set of black lights for about ten dollars from a costume supplier. If you do decide to do this, you will want to make some of your costume additions from fabrics that have been treated to shine under black lights. I must warn you that you may meet with some initial opposition from certain of your performers who will object to having the lights turned out so that only the costumes will glow. "After all, my children and friends are coming to see *me*," will be the cry. If you let them see how beautiful a number is with costumes that glow in the dark, and if you assure them that the lights will go up immediately after each number so the performers can be seen, the opposition will most likely join you! Two or three numbers well spaced during the show, plus the finale, would be about the correct proportion of black light numbers.

Costume additions for the various scenes might include
(1) bright boleros for one change, (2) hats and aprons,
matching, (3) large cummerbunds and bow ties, (4) hip-
length tunics that tie at the sides, and (5) top hats, gloves,
and canes for the last number. One group had as its final
song a toast to the audience. They held in their hands cham-
pagne glasses which had been sprayed with pink irridescent
paint. The effect under the black lights was magnificent.

Many of your group will be delighted to assist with the
sewing of the costumes, whether they are going to be in the
show or not. Some of the men will be good at making props
and scenery. Be sure to make your needs known to all of your
residents or members. People who may hesitate to participate
in any activity which requires them to work with a group or
before an audience may be eager to do things behind the
scenes or in their own rooms. Wherever possible, encourage
individuality and creativity in design. Be ready with suggestions as to how things might be done, but invite new ideas
and modifications from the one who is doing the work.

Some realtives and friends will consider it a privilege and
a pleasure to help backstage with costumes, props, lineups,
cues, etc. Invite them to at least one rehearsal so they will
know exactly what is expected of them. Plan to spend a few
moments privately with everybody who will be helping with
the performance and the performers. Make certain that they
understand the basic philosophy behind the entire project.
Explain that perfection is not the goal, but rather participation and a warm experience for all who are involved.

The helpers should be made aware that many of the goals
have already been attained in the preparations thus far. The
cooperation and good fellowship that have already been experienced during the weeks of rehearsal and costume and
scenery prepartions have been rewarding to all who were involved. Stress the importance of a completely relaxed atmosphere backstage throughout the performance. No one should
be made to feel tense or hurried. Everyone must have the

feeling that you have unqualified confidence in his ability to perform well, and that whatever he does will be good. Try to avoid mistakes that might cause embarrassment to the performers by having helpers "in the know" (residents or volunteers) strategically placed in the lineups and at the stage exits and entrances. Thus they can guide people to their proper places and initiate dance steps, etc. Make light of any errors that do occur and they will be quickly forgotten.

Charming numbers can be developed by allowing some members of the cast to select a favorite vocal recording. They then study it sufficiently so they can mouth the words and do some appropriate actions in perfect timing. Hopefully you can have the use of a small phonograph. If you do, the studying can be done in the privacy of one's own room. This eliminates the need for sacrificing group rehearsal time and boring them with endless repetition of the same number. This type of act should be attempted only by one who has a real knack for it and enjoys preparing for it.

Everybody enjoys rhythm bands, and one should certainly be a part of your show. They can use either kitchen utensils, or cymbals, drums, rhythm sticks, and tambourines, sometimes homemade. Even the deaf can keep time to the beat with a good conductor in full view.

The advantages to having a show like this are the stimulation and excitement it brings to a sometime drab existence in a sheltered atomsphere. It promotes a feeling of teamwork and togetherness which frequently spreads to other aspects of life in the home. It allows for creative self-expression which may have been lacking in the lives of some residents for years. For some people, it may be the first time they have ever had the opportunity to "ham it up." It can afford recognition and a feeling of personal worth to men and women who may have been convinced those days were gone forever.

INDEX